THE RIFF SERIES

Jazz Riffs for Bass.

by Rick Laird

GW00674812

Amsco Publications
New York/London/Sydney

Dedication

To Anita and Lotti

Note
The author welcomes any communication regarding the
material in this book. All mail to the publisher will
be forwarded.

Cover design by Pearce Marchbank
Cover photography by Gered Mankowitz
Edited by Peter Pickow and Jason Shulman

International Standard Book Number: 0.8256.2205.0

Exclusive Distributors:
Music Sales Corporation
24 East 22nd Street, New York, NY 10010 USA
Music Sales Limited
8/9 Frith Street, London W1V 5TZ England
Music Sales Pty. Limited
120 Rothschild Street, Rosebery, Sydney, NSW 2018, Australia

Printed in the United States of America by
Vicks Lithograph and Printing Corporation

Contents

Introduction

The following material has been compiled to provide both the student and the advanced bassist with musically stimulating ideas to aid in developing a fluent solo technique in the jazz idiom. In order to create meaningful, musical statements over chord progressions, it is necessary to have a firm knowledge of the scale related to each type of chord. I have included a Chord Scale Chart which contains the most frequently used chords.

By far, the best way to gain insight into soloing is to *listen* to players whose music you have an affinity for; don't restrict your listening to bassists, include *all* instruments. A solo is made up of musical ideas flowing smoothly from one to the next and making a statement, similar to vocal conversation. By listening to skilled artists and following their solos from beginning to conclusion, one can see how ideas develop and connect.

All of the material covered applies equally well to electric and acoustic bass, though certain techniques (double stops, etc.) are more accessible on electric. Since fingerings for acoustic and electric bass are different, they have not been included so as to avoid confusion. By figuring out the possible fingerings and positions for the music in this book, the student will gain valuable insight which can be directly applied towards forming his or her own approach to soloing and playing in general. Each musical phrase has been designed to act as a springboard for generating further ideas and to clearly demonstrate the different scale materials available for improvisation.

Note that jazz eighth notes are interpreted as follows:

$$\prod = \overset{\ulcorner 3 \urcorner}{\downarrow \flat}$$

This is a triple-meter feeling as opposed to rock eighth notes which are usually felt in duple meter and played evenly.

Chord Scale Chart

This chart shows the different scales available for improvising, creating melodies, and chord construction. Although these are by no means the only possible scales for jazz improvisation, they are some of the most frequently used. It is well worth the effort to learn them thoroughly and transpose them to all keys.

Symbols: △ =Major, – =Minor, + =Augmented, ○ =Diminished

* -7 (♭5) Chords can also use Half Diminished scale. For example:

C-7(♭5) (Symbol ∅)

Lydian (♭7) Scale

Lydian (♭7) scales are especially useful as substitutions. For instance, you can use the D♭7 lydian scale as a substitution for the G7 altered scale; they contain the same notes. E♭7 lydian is a substitution for A7 altered, F7 lydian for B7 altered, A♭7 lydian for D7 altered, B♭7 lydian for E7 altered, etc. Using the lydian (♭7) scale in this way will give you a different root motion and smoother chord progression. The following shows how lydian (♭7) scales can occur in the key of C major.

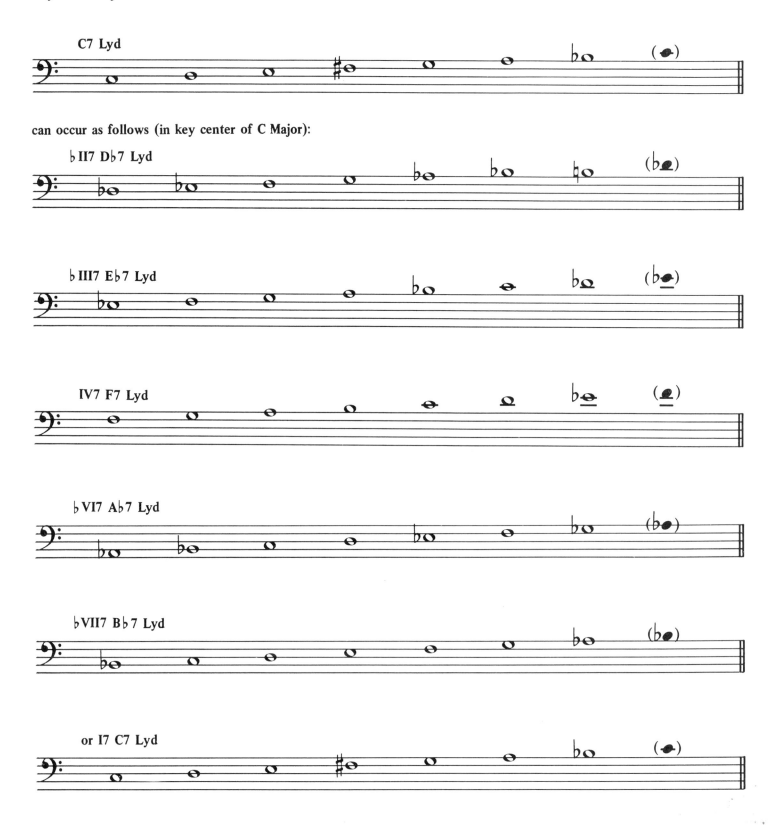

can occur as follows (in key center of C Major):

Method for Practicing Chord Scales

The example below should be applied to each of the chord scales and transposed
to all keys. This will greatly increase your fluency in handling bass lines and
solos in any key.

Example:

Practice Slow-Medium-Fast

Pentatonic (5–Note) Scale

Pentatonic (5-note) scales are very common in all forms of contemporary music.
They are easily applied to bass, both for soloing and creating jazz/rock figures.
Each chord scale contains one or more pentatonic scales. The section "Figures
from Pentatonics within Scales" deals with the various ways these can be used.
As always, transpose and play in all keys.

Some frequently used pentatonic scales:

① **Diatonic** ② **Pelog** ③ **Hirajoshi** ④ **Kumoi**

Each scale has it's modal inversion as follows:

① **Diatonic**

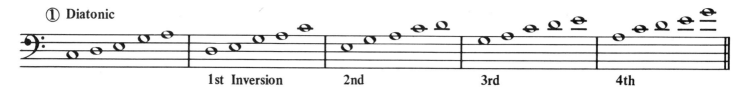

1st Inversion   **2nd**   **3rd**   **4th**

② **Pelog**

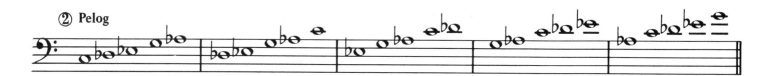

③ **Hirajoshi**

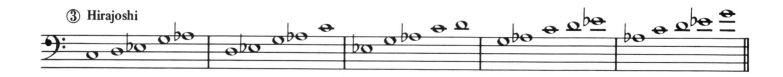

④ **Kumoi**

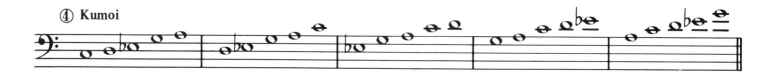

For an example of pentatonic scales in improvisation listen to John Coltrane's *Giant Steps* (Atlantic 1311).

Modes

The use of modal scales in jazz is quite common. They present a way of sustaining musical vitality while remaining on one scale or tonic point for long durations. A good example of a bass solo using the dorian mode is the tune "So What" played by Paul Chambers on Miles Davis's *Kind of Blue* (Columbia PC-8163). Transpose and play these modes in all keys.

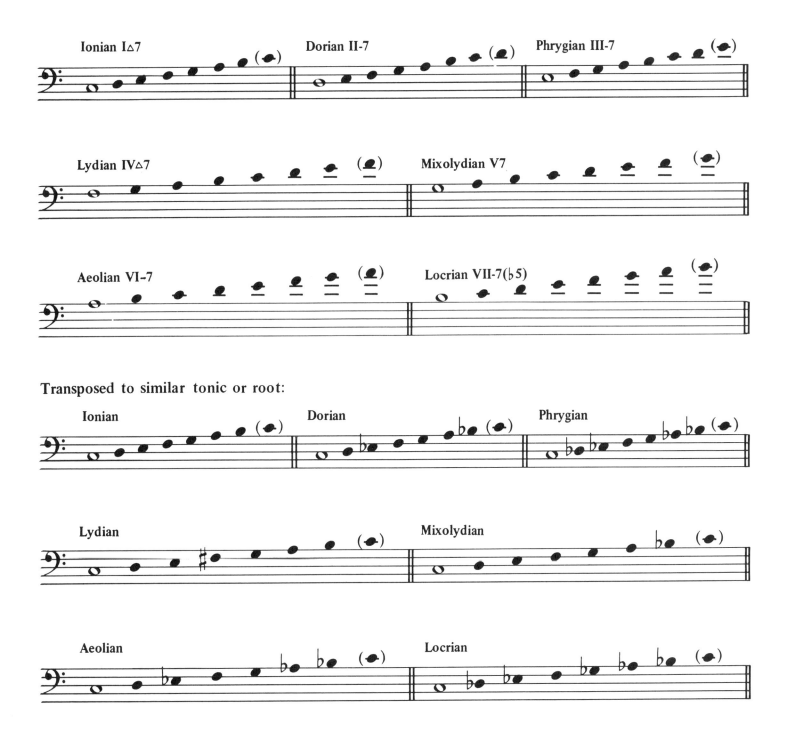

Transposed to similar tonic or root:

Figures from Pentatonics within Scales

These examples are designed to give the student an insight into using chord scales, and the pentatonics within, to create bass solos with meaningful, musical statements. They will also help you to acquire skill in reading this type of music. After playing each example, the student should make up his or her own figure on the particular chord scale; use the written figure as a springboard. It is helpful to write these out to make them totally clear to yourself, then to play them in various keys.

Figures from Pentatonics within Scales

* Retrograde

* Retrograde=Backwards

Lydian (♭7) Chords in Key Center of E Major

19

Sequential Patterns

3rd's (Major and Minor)

2nd's (Major)

2nd's (Minor)

6th (Major) 5th Added

6th's (Minor) 7th and 11th Added

Connecting Chords

The majority of standards and jazz compositions consist of chords joined together to form a logical progression of harmonic movement. While there are numerous ways to form chord progressions, some types of chord movement can be considered to be patterns. These patterns appear in many contemporary compositions. II-7 V7 I is very common as is I VI-7 V7 I. I have given examples of the first of these patterns only. The second pattern is the same except for the addition of the VI-7 (usually implying the aeolian mode).

A less common and often misunderstood progression is I VI7 II-7 V7 I. A full explanation and examples of this pattern are included.

Connecting Chords

II-7 V7 I in Major Keys

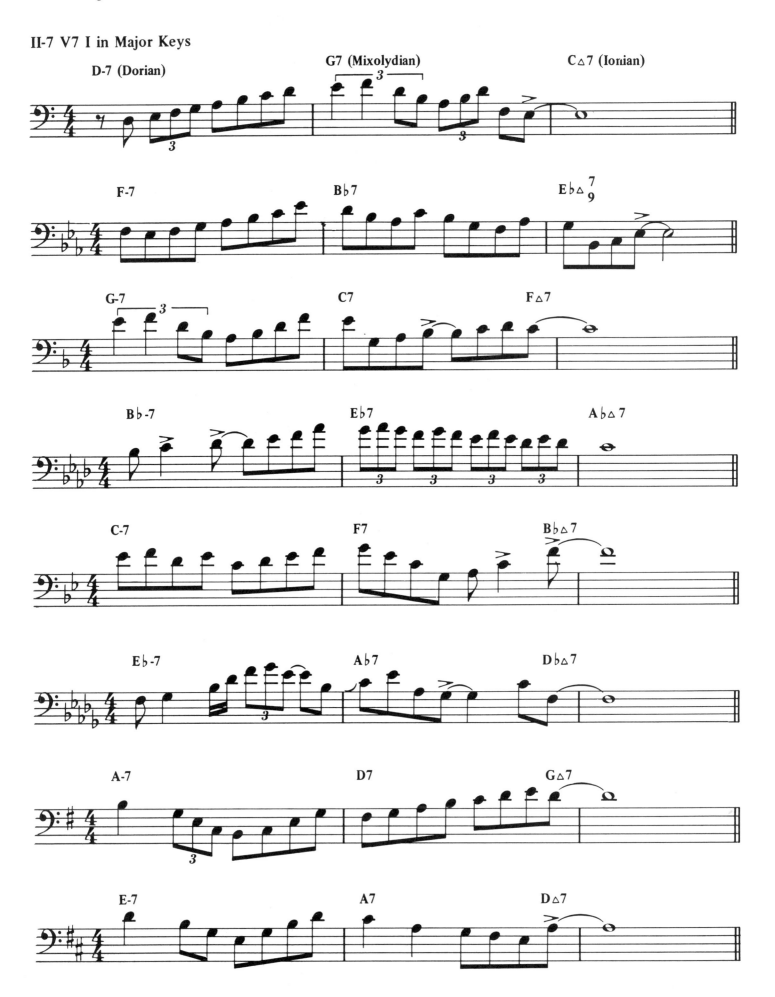

II-7 V7 I in Minor Keys

I VI7 II-7 V7 I in Major Keys

V7 in Major
Key of C

Choice of scale depends on melody notes or chord voicings used.

With substitute chords: I ♭III7 II-7 ♭II7

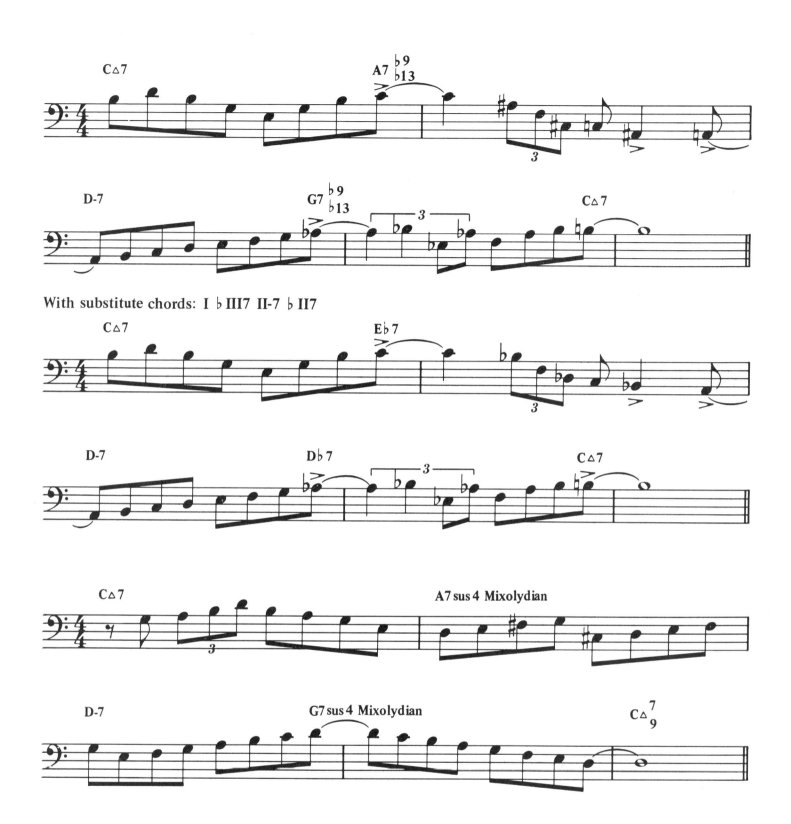

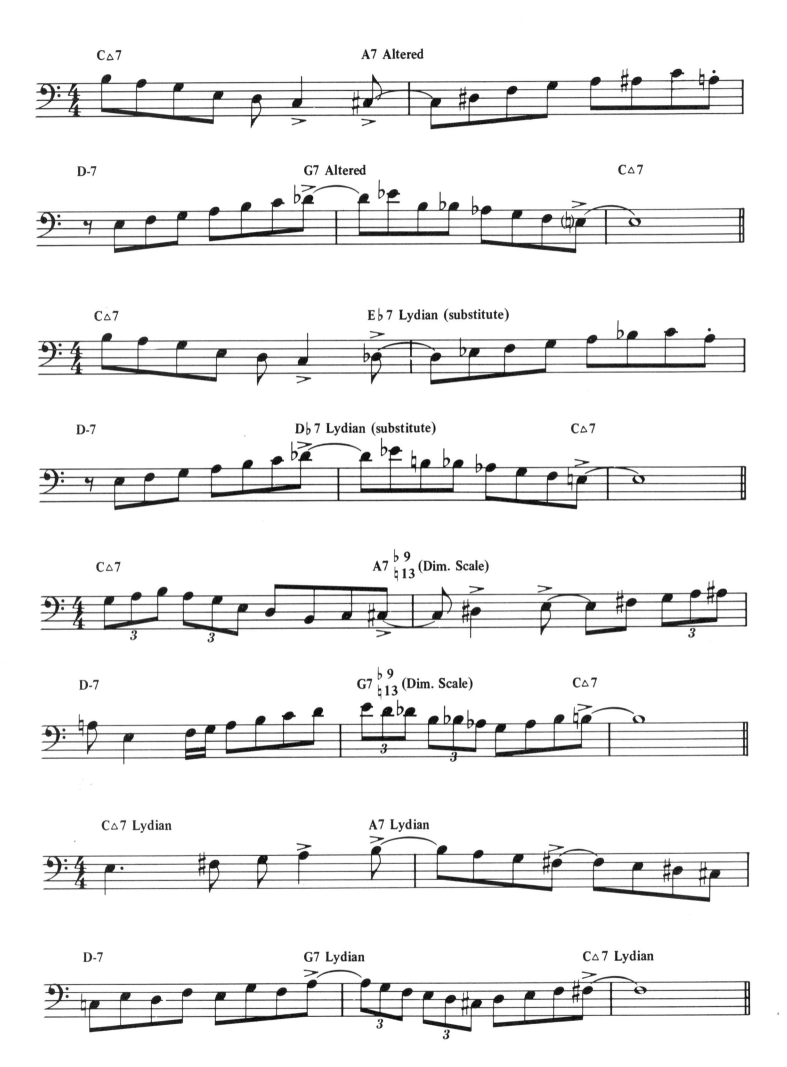

Odd Time Signatures (Rock)

Odd time signatures have recently become quite common in jazz fusion music. While most jazz and pop music is in $\frac{4}{4}$ time, playing in odd time signatures ($\frac{7}{4}$, $\frac{10}{8}$, etc.) is a lot of fun and offers a real musical challenge. Their use in ethnic musics; Indian, Greek, Turkish, etc.; goes back many hundreds of years. To gain insight into this form, listen to some Indian master musicians like Ravi Shankar or Ali Akbar Khan.

Odd Time Signatures (Rock)

For further examples of odd time signatures listen to *Inner Mounting Flame*
by Mahavishnu Orchestra (Columbia PC-31067).

Blues

Present Time Blues

Rick Laird

Solo on "Present Time Blues" Progression

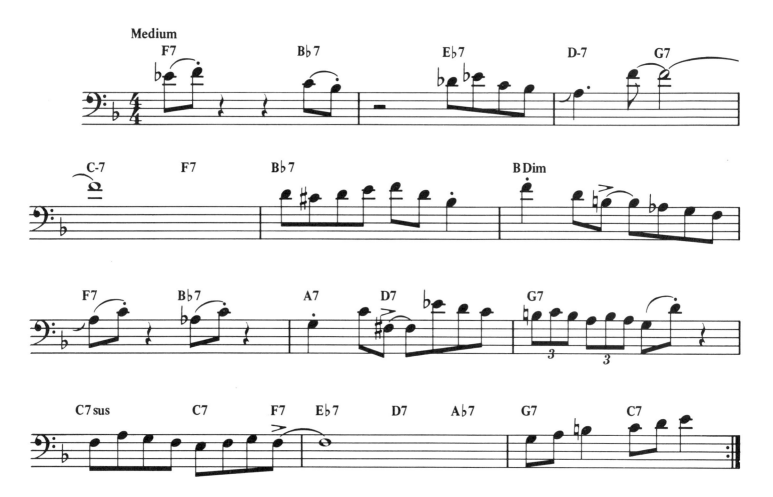

Modal Jazz

Mode Ode

Rick Laird

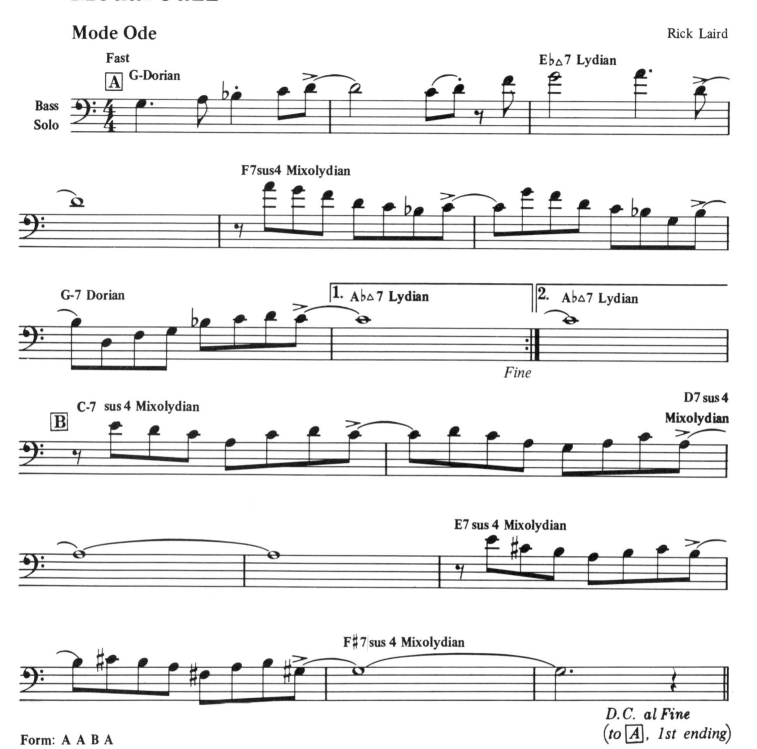

Form: A A B A

Solo on "Mode Ode" Progression

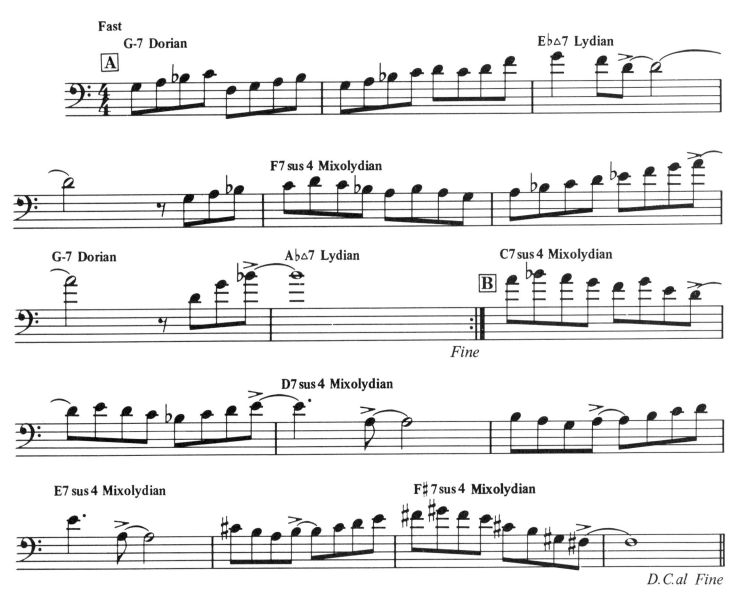

String Snaps and Double Stops

The string "snap" is a useful percussive effect that can be accomplished by:
(a) Placing the thumb slightly under the string at the end of the fingerboard,
raising the string and releasing it so that it snaps against the fingerboard; (b)
By striking the string with the side of the thumb; or (c) By using the thumb and
the 1st finger to raise and release the string. A plus sign (+) is used to designate
snapped notes.

Double stops are plucked with the thumb and 1st finger.

Double Stops (Bass Guitar)

Pluck with thumb and first finger of right hand on E string and G string.

Unaccompanied Bass Guitar

This composition shows some of the ways that the bass guitar can be used as a solo instrument. It has been written in the treble clef to avoid excessive leger lines in the bass clef. The 3-note chords can be plucked simultaneously with the thumb, 1st, and 2nd fingers or strummed with the thumb. The piece is written for a bass with a 24-fret neck.

As this is a relatively new use of the bass guitar, the student is urged to experiment and find his or her own way to create similar uses for the instrument. An excellent example of an unaccompanied bass guitar solo can be heard in a composition entitled "Portrait of Tracy" on the album *Jaco Pastorius* (Epic PE-33949).

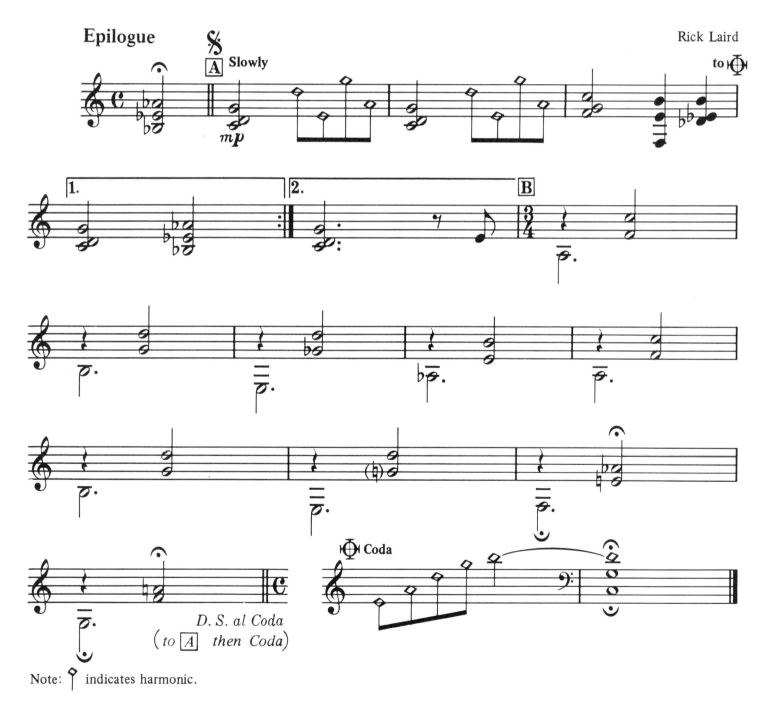

Note: ♾ indicates harmonic.

Bibliography

Theory

Paul Hindemith, *Elementary Training for Musicians* (Schott/dist. by Belwin Mills)

Vincent Persichetti, *Twentieth-Century Harmony* (Norton)

Nicholas Slonimsky, *Thesaurus of Scales & Melodic Patterns* (Scribner)

Ray Brown, *Ray Brown Bass Method*

Music

J. S. Bach, *Two-Part Inventions* (for reading)

J. S. Bach, *371 Chorales* (for harmony)

Discography

Jaco Pastorius	*Jaco Pastorius*	Epic PE-33949
	Heavy Weather (Weather Report)	Columbia PC-34418
Stanley Clarke	*School Days*	Nemperor 439
	Journey to Love	Nemperor 433
Eberhard Weber	*Colours of Chloe*	ECM 1042
Will Lee	*Brecker Bros.*	Arista 4037
Scott La Faro	*Portrait in Jazz* (Bill Evans Trio)	Riverside 12-312
Ron Carter	*E.S.P.* (Miles Davis)	Columbia PC-9150
	Nefertiti (Miles Davis)	Columbia PC-9594
Paul Chambers	*Kind of Blue* (Miles Davis)	Columbia PC-8163
Rick Laird	*Inner Mounting Flame* (Mahavishnu Orchestra)	Columbia PC-31067
	Birds of Fire (Mahavishnu Orchestra)	Columbia PC- & PCQ-31996
	Between Nothingness and Eternity (Mahavishnu Orchestra)	Columbia C- & CQ-32766
	Rick Laird—Soft Focus	Timeless Records (Holland)
	Still on the Planet (Eddie Jefferson)	Muse 5063
	New York Afternoon (Richie Cole)	Muse 5119
	Brief Encounter (Eddie Daniels)	Muse